Summer Success® Math

Patsy F. Kanter • Andy Clark • Barbara B. Irvin

GReaT SOuRCe®
EDUCATION GROUP
A Houghton Mifflin Company

Credits

Design/Production: Taurins Design

Illustration Credits: Steven Mach *pages 35, 47, 69, 75, 77, 87, 95 109, 113, 117.*

Printed in the United States of America

Great Source® and *Summer Success*® are registered trademarks of Houghton Mifflin Company.

International Standard Book Number: 0-669-48444-X

2 3 4 5 6 7 8 9 10 MZ 06 05 04 03 02

Visit our web site: http://www.greatsource.com/

Name _____

Choose or write the best answer for each question.

1. Shade $\frac{2}{3}$ of this set.

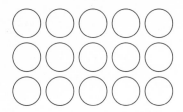

2. Draw a line that is $\frac{1}{4}$ the length of this line.

3. Write the simplest fraction, a decimal, and a percent to show what part of the grid below is shaded.

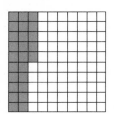

_____, _____, _____

4. Write another expression for $4 \times 4 \times 4$.

_____

5. Use $<$, $>$, or $=$ to compare the numbers.

5 _____ ⁻5

6. Write $\frac{7}{8}$ as a decimal.

_____

7. Which expression represents 450,000,000?

Ⓐ $(4 \times 10^9) + (5 \times 10^8)$

Ⓑ $(4 \times 10^8) + (5 \times 10^7)$

Ⓒ $(4 \times 10^7) + (5 \times 10^6)$

Ⓓ $(4 \times 10^6) + (5 \times 10^5)$

Ⓔ $(4 \times 10^5) + (5 \times 10^4)$

8. What is the prime factorization of 36?

Ⓐ 3×6 Ⓓ $2^3 \times 3^2$

Ⓑ 2×3 Ⓔ $2^3 \times 3^3$

Ⓒ $2^2 \times 3^2$

9. What is the value of 9^2?

Ⓐ 11   Ⓓ 81

Ⓑ 18   Ⓔ 92

Ⓒ 29

10. $\frac{5}{12} + \frac{2}{3} =$

Ⓐ $\frac{7}{15}$ Ⓓ $\frac{2}{3}$

Ⓑ $\frac{5}{18}$ Ⓔ $1\frac{1}{12}$

Ⓒ $\frac{10}{36}$

11. Show ⁻1 + ⁻1 + ⁻1 on the number line.

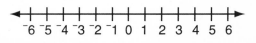

12. What is the value of this expression?

$^-7 + 3 \times 4 \div 2$

(A) $^-8$ (D) 13

(B) $^-2$ (E) 20

(C) $^-1$

---

13. What is the value of this expression?

$4.0 \times 10^3 \times 3.0 \times 10^2$

(A) 1.2×10^5

(B) 1.2×10^6

(C) 7.0×10^5

(D) 12.0×10^3

(E) 12.0×10^6

---

14. $\frac{2}{3}$ of two dozen eggs is how many eggs?

(A) $1\frac{1}{3}$ (D) 9

(B) 4   (E) 16

(C) 8

---

15. What is the measure of the missing angle?

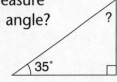

_____

---

16. The two rectangles below are similar. What is the length of the missing side of the smaller rectangle?

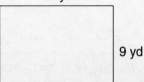

12 yd

4 yd

?   9 yd

_____

---

17. Connect the points (2, 3), (2, 1), ($^-$1, 1), and ($^-$1, 3) in order on the grid. What quadrilateral is made?

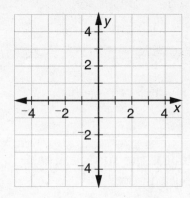

_____

---

18. Draw a reflection of the figure shown across the x-axis. Write the ordered pairs of the new figure.

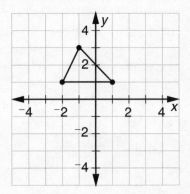

(_____, _____), (_____, _____),

and (_____, _____)

---

19. Which figure has exactly 5 faces?

(A) triangular pyramid

(B) triangular prism

(C) rectangular prism

(D) pentagon

(E) cube

20. What is the circumference of this circle? Use π = 3.14.

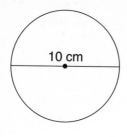

- **(A)** 15.7 cm
- **(B)** 31.4 cm
- **(C)** 62.8 cm
- **(D)** 78.5 cm
- **(E)** 314 cm

10 cm

21. What is the surface area of this figure?

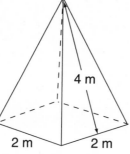

- **(A)** 4 m²
- **(B)** 16 m²
- **(C)** 20 m²
- **(D)** 40 m²
- **(E)** 64 m²

4 m

2 m   2 m

22. What is the volume of this cylinder? Use π = 3.14.

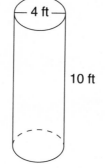

- **(A)** 20 ft³
- **(B)** 40 ft³
- **(C)** 62.8 ft³
- **(D)** 125.6 ft³
- **(E)** 502.4 ft³

4 ft

10 ft

23. If the pattern continues, what is the perimeter of the 6th figure?

- **(A)** 15 units
- **(B)** 20 units
- **(C)** 21 units
- **(D)** 24 units
- **(E)** 28 units

24. Write the next two numbers in this sequence.

$\frac{5}{6}$, $1\frac{2}{3}$, $2\frac{1}{2}$, _____, _____

25. If $n \times n \times n = 27$, $n =$

- **(A)** 25
- **(B)** 18
- **(C)** 9
- **(D)** 6
- **(E)** 3

26. In the figure below, one apple weighs as much as how many bananas?

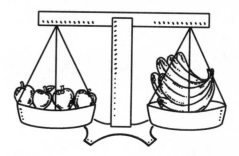

- **(A)** $\frac{2}{3}$
- **(B)** $\frac{3}{4}$
- **(C)** $1\frac{1}{6}$
- **(D)** $1\frac{1}{3}$
- **(E)** $1\frac{1}{2}$

27. A store has a $\frac{1}{4}$-off sale. If the regular price of a T-shirt is $16, what is the cost of three T-shirts on sale?

_____

28. A rectangle has a perimeter of 60 feet. The width is $\frac{1}{2}$ the length. What are the dimensions of the rectangle?

length: _____

width: _____

29. Kevin bought 2 pens and 2 erasers for $1.50. Lynn bought 1 pen and 1 notebook for $1.50. Maria bought 2 notebooks for $2.20. How much did Neal pay for 4 erasers? Show your work.

_____

_____

_____

30. What is the probability of spinning either a 2 or a 5 on this spinner?

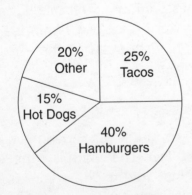

(A) $\frac{21}{6}$

(B) $\frac{1}{3}$

(C) $\frac{1}{9}$

(D) $\frac{1}{2}$

(E) $\frac{1}{36}$

31. The 400 seventh-grade students at Wilson Middle School voted to see which food was their favorite. The results are shown in the graph below. How many students liked tacos as their favorite food?

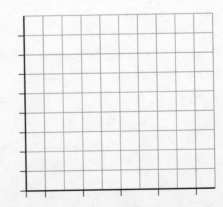

_____

32. Which statement is true? Use the graph to choose the best answer.

Average Winning Speeds Indianapolis 500 Auto Race

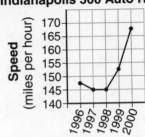

(A) Average speeds in 1997 and 1998 were about the same.

(B) Average speeds increase each year.

(C) Cars cannot exceed 170 miles per hour.

(D) All of the above

(E) None of the above

33. Make a double-line graph to display the data in the table below. Label your graph, give it a title, and include a key.

Students in School Media Center

	Mon.	Tues.	Wed.	Thurs.	Fri.
Girls	50	45	60	65	25
Boys	70	45	55	40	15

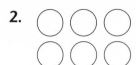

Name_____

028

Shade each model to show $\frac{1}{2}$.

1.

2.

3.

014

Write the word form for each number.

4. 0.5 _____

5. 0.50 _____

6. 1.5 _____

104

Continue the pattern and answer the related questions.

7. $\frac{1}{2}$, 1, $1\frac{1}{2}$, 2, _____, _____, _____,

8. If the pattern above continues, what is the tenth term? _____

9. Describe the pattern in question 7. _____

032

Solve the problem.

10. A store has a $\frac{1}{2}$-off sale on sweatshirts. If the original price is $45.00,

how much does a sweatshirt cost on sale? _____

DRAW

WRITE

_____

_____

_____

_____

_____

_____

_____

028 **Shade each model to show $\frac{1}{3}$.**

1.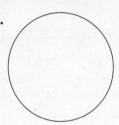

2.

3.

014 **Write the word form for each number.**

4. 0.33 _____

5. 0.333 _____

6. 0.3333 _____

032 **Solve the problems.**

7. One student has $12.00. Another student has $\frac{1}{3}$ less. How much money does the second student have? _____

8. Currently, $\frac{1}{3}$ of Shira's coin collection is quarters. She has twelve quarters from the Denver mint. This is $\frac{1}{3}$ of all the quarters in her collection. How many coins does Shira have altogether? _____

DRAW

WRITE

_____
_____
_____
_____
_____
_____
_____
_____

 MATERIALS

Three-ring binders and loose-leaf paper, or spiral notebooks, colored markers

 GLOSSARY TO GO

Today you will begin to create a math glossary to be used in school and at home. It will contain pictures and definitions of many math terms that you will encounter in math texts and tests. By writing your own definitions and keeping them in a notebook, you will be more likely to remember and understand these terms. You can use the glossary throughout the summer and as a resource during the next school year.

Begin by designing a cover for your ring binder or spiral notebook. The glossary works best if you use 26 sheets of paper, each headed by a letter of the alphabet for quick reference.

Each day, you will write definitions and draw pictures illustrating the terms. The vocabulary should be covered in your class time, so you should be familiar with most of the terms.

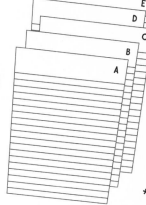

* 442, 424

◆ **Vocabulary**

Define each term in your glossary. Draw a picture or give an example of each term.

- Percent
- Ratio

 HOME CONNECTION

These problems and games should be done at home. Sometimes you will need a family member or friend to help you.

143–148, 032

◆ **Staying Sharp**

Ask a family member or friend to ask you these problems orally. Answer them as quickly as possible. See if you can do them even faster the second time.

$5 \times 7 =$ _____	$10 \times 5 =$ _____	$\frac{1}{2}$ of $16 =$ _____
$6 \times 7 =$ _____	$10 \times 7 =$ _____	$\frac{1}{2}$ of $24 =$ _____
$7 \times 7 =$ _____	$10 \times 9 =$ _____	$\frac{1}{2}$ of $50 =$ _____
$8 \times 7 =$ _____	$10 \times 10 =$ _____	$\frac{1}{2}$ of $66 =$ _____
$9 \times 7 =$ _____	$10 \times 11 =$ _____	$\frac{1}{2}$ of $98 =$ _____

* The tabs on every Make & Take page tell you where to find additional hints, definitions, or explanations in the mathematics handbook *Math on Call*. For information on ordering *Math on Call* visit www.greatsource.com or call 800-289-4490.

Roll a Fraction

◆ **MATERIALS**

One 1–6 number cube, paper, pencils

◆ **DIRECTIONS**

1. The object of the game is to get an answer equal to or as close as possible to $\frac{1}{2}$.

2. Players make a recording sheet like the one shown.

3. Player 1 rolls the number cube, noting the number, and then rolls the cube again. Player 1 uses the two digits to make a fraction. For example, with 3 and 4, $\frac{3}{4}$ or $\frac{4}{3}$ can be made.

4. Player 1 finds $\frac{1}{2}$ of this fraction and writes it down. The object is to get as close as possible to $\frac{1}{2}$. For example, if Player 1 rolls a 4 and then another 4, he or she can make the fraction $\frac{4}{4}$, multiply by $\frac{1}{2}$ and get exactly $\frac{1}{2}$.

5. Player 2 repeats this procedure. Then players compare and decide who is closer to $\frac{1}{2}$. The player who is closer to $\frac{1}{2}$ wins the round and gets one point. In case of a tie in a round, both players get one point.

6. The first player to win three rounds wins the game.

Roll a Fraction

Player 1 _____   Player 2 _____

Fraction	X $\frac{1}{2}$	Fraction	X $\frac{1}{2}$	Winner
Round 1				
Round 2				
Round 3				

PRACTICE

028

Shade each model to show $\frac{1}{4}$.

1. [ ]

2. ○○○○
   ○○○○
   ○○○○
   ○○○○

3. [ ]

044, 442

Write $\frac{1}{4}$ two different ways.

4. As a decimal. _____

5. As a percent. _____

160–163, 346

Use the drawing to answer questions 6 and 7.

6. The width of this rectangle is $\frac{1}{4}$ the length.
   If the width is $1\frac{1}{2}$ inches, what is the length? _____

7. What is the perimeter of this rectangle? _____

132–135

Continue the pattern and answer the related questions.

8. $5\frac{3}{4}$, $5\frac{1}{2}$, $5\frac{1}{4}$, 5, _____, _____, _____,

9. Which terms are whole numbers in the pattern in question 8?

   _____

10. Which term is 3 in the pattern in question 8? _____

11. Which term is 0 in the pattern in question 8? _____

DRAW

WRITE

_____
_____
_____
_____
_____
_____
_____
_____

GLOSSARY TO GO

◀ Vocabulary

Define each term in your glossary. Draw a picture or give an example of each term.

- Terminating decimal
- Repeating decimal

Glossary to Go

593, 025, 023

HOME CONNECTION

◀ Staying Sharp

Ask someone at home to read these problems to you. See how quickly you can solve them mentally.

99 + 56 = _____

201 − 155 = _____

999 + 121 = _____

10,001 − 500 = _____

0.9 + 0.6 = _____

1.1 − 0.5 = _____

088–090, 116–119

A dime is what percent of a dollar? _____

A quarter is what percent of a dollar? _____

A penny is what percent of a dollar? _____

A nickel is what percent of a dollar? _____

442

Three quarters is what percent of a dollar? _____

73 cents is what percent of a dollar? _____

Twelve dimes is what percent of a dollar? _____

Shade each model to show $\frac{1}{5}$.

1.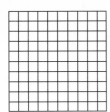

2.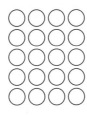

3.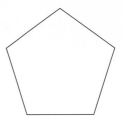

Write $\frac{1}{5}$ two different ways.

4. As a decimal. _____

5. As a percent. _____

Use the drawing to answer question 6.

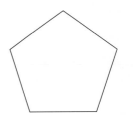

6. If one side of this regular pentagon is $1\frac{1}{5}$ cm,

   what is the perimeter? _____

Continue the pattern and answer the related question.

7. $\frac{1}{10}, \frac{1}{5}, \frac{3}{10}, \frac{2}{5}, \frac{1}{2},$ _____, _____, _____,

8. Rewrite the pattern in question 7 using fractions with a common denominator.

_____, _____, _____, _____, _____, _____, _____, _____,

DRAW

WRITE

_____

_____

_____

_____

_____

_____

_____

MAKE & TAKE

GLOSSARY TO GO

Vocabulary

Define each term in your glossary. Draw a picture or give an example of each term.

- Line of symmetry
- Proportion

389, 429

HOME CONNECTION

Game

Try this simple game with a friend. Have your friend—

1. Pick a number.
2. Multiply it by 4.
3. Add 2 to the product.
4. Divide the sum by 2.
5. Subtract the original number.
6. Subtract the original number again.

Close your eyes and pretend to be concentrating very hard. Then tell your friend that the resulting answer is 1.

For example, say the number your friend picks is 9.

$9 \times 4 = 36; 36 + 2 = 38; 38 \div 2 = 19; 19 - 9 = 10; 10 - 9 = 1$

Try this several times to see if it works with any number your friend picks.

Try to figure out why this works. Try thinking of the number your friend picks as one basket containing that number of jelly beans. Multiplying by 4 makes four of those baskets. Adding 2 makes four baskets and two jelly beans. Dividing by 2 leaves two baskets and one jelly bean. Subtracting the original number means removing one basket. Subtracting it again means there are no more baskets and only 1 jelly bean remains.

491

Staying Sharp

List all the factors of these numbers.

12 _____

20 _____

24 _____

30 _____

56 _____

60 _____

056

Fraction Sums

◆ MATERIALS

One 1–6 number cube, paper, pencils

◆ DIRECTIONS

1. The object of the game is to get a sum equal to or as close as possible to a target number by adding five fractions.

2. Make a recording sheet like the one shown. Players begin with the number 3 as the target sum.

3. Player 1 rolls the number cube twice and uses the two digits to make a fraction. For example, with 2 and 3, $\frac{2}{3}$ or $\frac{3}{2}$ can be made. That player records the fraction in the appropriate column of the recording sheet. Player 2 repeats this procedure. Beginning with the second turn, each player makes a new fraction, adds it to the fraction made in the previous turn, and records the sum.

4. Players alternate turns until each player has made and added five fractions. At that point, players compare their sums to decide who is closer to the target sum. The player who is closer to the target wins the game.

5. After several games, you may change the target number.

Fraction Sums

	Target Sum	Player 1 _____		Player 2 _____	
		Fraction	Sum	Fraction	Sum
Roll 1			/////		/////
Roll 2					
Roll 3					
Roll 4					
Roll 5					

Today's Number: $\frac{1}{6}$

Name _____

028 Shade each model to show $\frac{1}{6}$.

1.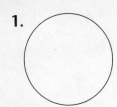

2.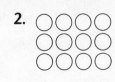

3.

044, 442 Write $\frac{1}{6}$ two different ways.

4. As a decimal. _____

5. As a percent. _____

026, 442 Continue the pattern.

6. $16\frac{2}{3}\%$, $33\frac{1}{3}\%$, 50%, $66\frac{2}{3}\%$, _____, _____, _____,

442 Solve the problem.

7. Which is less money, $\frac{1}{6}$ of $100 or $\frac{1}{3}$ of $50? _____

143–148 Circle the equations that are true.

8. $10 \times 2 \times 8 = 20 \times 4 \times 2$

9. $\frac{100}{3} \times 30 = \frac{30}{3} \times 100$

10. $\frac{1}{2} \times 50 \times 4 = \frac{1}{4} \times 100 \times 2 \times 2$

11. $\frac{1}{4} \times 8 \div 2 = 2 \times 8 \times \frac{1}{4}$

12. $\frac{1}{6} \times 2 \times 4 = \frac{1}{3} \times 2 \times 2$

13. $5 \times 3 \times 2 + 25 = 5 \times 3 + 2 \times 25$

DRAW

WRITE

_____
_____
_____
_____
_____
_____
_____
_____
_____

MAKE & TAKE

GLOSSARY TO GO

▲ **Vocabulary**

Define each term in your glossary. Draw a picture or give an example of each term.

• Pentagon

• Abbreviations: cm

m

HOME CONNECTION

Ask someone at home to read these problems to you. Answer them as quickly as possible.

◆ **Staying Sharp**

$10 \times 4 =$ _____ $40 \div 10 =$ _____

$10 \times 4.1 =$ _____ $4 \div 10 =$ _____

$100 \times 4.1 =$ _____ $4 \div 100 =$ _____

$8 \times 8 =$ _____

$8 \times 9 =$ _____

$9 \times 9 =$ _____

◆ **Write About It**

• What is the most difficult multiplication fact for you to remember? Write down two suggestions for how to figure it out if you forget.

  For example,

  ONE WAY: 8×7 is 56 because 4×7 is 28 and twice that is 56.

  ANOTHER WAY: 8×7 is 56 because $10 \times 7 = 70$, $2 \times 7 = 14$, and $70 - 14 = 56$.

• Look in a newspaper or magazine to find a fraction, decimal or percent. It can be in a story or in an advertisement. Copy down the example.

Weekly Newsletter

Each day your child will be bringing home material that reviews and extends math concepts studied in class. These will include problems for your child to solve alone and games or other activities that will allow you to help your child explore mathematical concepts.

Your child has completed the first week of the Summer Success Math program. This program is designed to teach your child the basics of mathematics—arithmetic, measurement, geometry, statistics—as well as to reason and think mathematically. In class, students are asked to justify their answers, to reason, and to solve problems using a variety of approaches.

The math your child will need to know in her or his future is of great importance. Good math skills are required in every job from electrician to computer scientist, from nurse to architect. When asked, employers list the following math skills as essential:

- the ability to use math to solve real-world problems
- the ability to interpret and analyze data
- the ability to use technology to solve problems

One of the most important languages of math is algebra. Algebra enables people to solve problems and to see patterns and relationships. This summer, your child will learn to think algebraically and therefore become a better problem solver and math student.

Your child will be studying about fractions, decimals and percents. This week, your child learned how to think about fractions as proportions that can be expressed in decimal and percent forms. For example, beginning with $\frac{1}{2}$, we studied the connections between 1 out of 2, 5 out of 10, 0.5, 50 out of 100, and 50%, which are all ways to talk about one half.

We then looked for patterns based on $\frac{1}{2}$, such as extending the pattern $\frac{1}{2}$, 1, $1\frac{1}{2}$, 2, and so on. Students played games that required them to multiply by $\frac{1}{2}$ and to understand the relative size of fractions. Understanding how to use fractions, percents, and decimals is necessary for everything from making wise financial decisions to using measuring tools. Help your child see how often fractions and percents are used in the world, in recipes, newspaper stories, tipping in a restaurant, or financing a car.

As part of the program, we reviewed some math vocabulary. The words we studied this week included—

- percent (A number that shows a fractional part of 100.)
- terminating and repeating decimals (Decimals that end, such as 0.5, and decimals that never end, like 0.33333333. . .)
- proportion (An equation showing two ratios that are equal, such as $\frac{1}{2} = \frac{2}{4}$.)
- metric measurements such as centimeter, meter, gram, and kilogram (A small paper clip weighs between 1 and 2 grams; a school dictionary weighs about 1 kilogram.)

Support your child's learning by asking if he or she can explain what these words mean. Showing interest and enthusiasm for math will help your child know that math is important to you, too.

PRACTICE

Name _____

Shade each model to show $\frac{2}{3}$.

1.

2. ○○○○○○○○○○
○○○○○○○○○○

028

Draw a line that is $\frac{2}{3}$ the length of this line.

3. ├─────────────────────┤

028

Write the word form for each number.

014

4. 0.66 _____

5. 0.666 _____

6. 0.6666 _____

Write $\frac{2}{3}$ two different ways.

044, 442

7. As a decimal. _____ **8.** As a percent. _____

Continue each pattern.

9. $33\frac{1}{3}$, $66\frac{2}{3}$, 100, $133\frac{1}{3}$, _____, _____, _____,

106

10. 1, $\frac{2}{3}$, $\frac{4}{9}$, _____, _____,

162

DRAW

WRITE

_____
_____
_____
_____
_____
_____
_____
_____

MAKE & TAKE

 GLOSSARY TO GO

◆ Vocabulary

Define each term in your glossary. Draw a picture or give an example of each term.

- Interior angle
- Exterior angle

HOME CONNECTION

◆ Game

You can play **Fraction Time** with a friend or family member at home. Use number or dot cubes if you have them. If not, make two sets of 1–6 number cards and put them in a paper bag. You'll also need paper and a pencil.

Directions

1. Make a recording sheet like the one shown.

2. Player 1 rolls the number cube twice, or draws two cards out of the paper bag, uses the digits to make a fraction less than or equal to one, and records the fraction. That player determines and records how many minutes are in that fractional part of one hour. For example, if 2 and 5 are rolled, $\frac{2}{5}$ is the only fraction that can be made, and $\frac{2}{5}$ of one hour is 24 minutes.

Fraction Time

Round		Player 1 _____	Player 2 _____
1	Fraction	$\frac{2}{5}$	$\frac{3}{5}$
	Minutes	24	36
2	Fraction		
	Minutes		
3	Fraction		
	Minutes		
4	Fraction		
	Minutes		
5	Fraction		
	Minutes		
Total:			

3. Player 2 receives the remaining minutes that make up one whole hour if that player correctly identifies what fractional part of one hour the minutes represent. For example, the 36 minutes remaining are $\frac{3}{5}$ of one hour. If Player 2 does not correctly identify the fraction, the remaining minutes go to Player 1.

4. Player 2 then rolls or draws two numbers and follows the same steps, with Player 1 receiving the remaining minutes after naming the correct fraction.

5. Play alternates back and forth until both players have had five turns.

6. Players add the minutes they have accumulated and convert the total to show hours and minutes. The winner is the player with more hours and minutes.

Fraction Time

◆ MATERIALS

One 1–6 number cube, paper, pencil

◆ DIRECTIONS

1. Players make a recording sheet like the one shown.

2. Player 1 rolls the number cube twice, uses the digits to make a fraction less than or equal to one, and records the fraction. He or she then determines and records how many minutes are in that fractional part of one hour. For example, if 2 and 5 are rolled, $\frac{2}{5}$ is the only fraction that can be made, and $\frac{2}{5}$ of one hour is 24 minutes.

3. Player 2 receives the remaining minutes that make up one whole hour if she or he correctly identifies what fractional part of one hour the minutes represent. For example, the 36 minutes remaining are $\frac{3}{5}$ of one hour. If Player 2 does not correctly identify the fraction, the remaining minutes go to Player 1.

4. Player 2 then rolls the number cube twice and follows the same steps, with Player 1 receiving the remaining minutes after naming the correct fraction.

5. Play alternates back and forth until both players have had five turns.

6. Players add the minutes they have accumulated and convert the total to show hours and minutes. The winner is the player with more hours and minutes.

Fraction Time

Round		Player 1 _____	Player 2 _____
1	Fraction	$\frac{2}{5}$	$\frac{3}{5}$
	Minutes	24	36
2	Fraction		
	Minutes		
3	Fraction		
	Minutes		
4	Fraction		
	Minutes		
5	Fraction		
	Minutes		
Total:			

Name _____

028 Shade each model to show $\frac{5}{6}$.

1.

2.

014 Write the word form for each number.

3. 0.8 _____

4. 0.833 _____

5. 0.8333 _____

044, 442 Write $\frac{5}{6}$ two different ways.

6. As a decimal. _____ 7. As a percent. _____

143–148 Use mental math to find each product. Write a brief explanation of your solution strategy.

8. $5 \times 12 =$ _____

9. $6 \times 18 =$ _____

10. $8 \times 15 =$ _____

161 Solve the problem.

11. Last night there were 14,400 people at a rock concert. Tonight $\frac{5}{6}$ of that many people are there. How many people are at the concert tonight? _____

DRAW

WRITE

_____

_____

_____

_____

_____

_____

_____

_____

376

MATERIALS

Vocabulary

Define each term in your glossary. Draw a picture or give an example of each term.

- Similar figure
- Regular figure

HOME CONNECTION

102, 131, 158, 184

Staying Sharp

Solve these problems on your own.

- In a three-day bike race, the bikers rode 50.5 kilometers on the first day, 40.5 km on the second day, and 67.7 km on the third day. How far did they ride in the three days? _____

- One bike weighs 12.6 kilograms and another bike weighs 9.8 kg. How much heavier is the first bike? _____

- One biker rode at an average speed of 10.1 km per hour. About how far did the biker ride in 5 hours? _____

- Another biker rode at an average speed of 15.1 km per hour. If the biker rode 120.8 km, about how many hours did the biker ride? _____

Write About It

- In a triangle, what is the sum of the interior angles? _____

- In a quadrilateral, what is the sum of the interior angles? _____

341–342

466

- Use the 1–6 number cards you made yesterday or two 1–6 number or dot cubes. Draw or roll two digits, make a fraction less than or equal to one, and record the fraction. Do this ten times. What fraction occurred most often? _____

Shade each model to show $\frac{6}{7}$.

028

1. [ ]

2. ◯◯◯◯◯◯◯
   ◯◯◯◯◯◯◯
   ◯◯◯◯◯◯◯

Write a decimal for each fraction. Round the number to the nearest thousandth.

030, 021

3. $\frac{1}{7}$ _____

4. $\frac{3}{7}$ _____

5. $\frac{6}{7}$ _____

Solve the problem.

161

6. Jose had $42.00. He earned $\frac{6}{7}$ of that amount doing odd jobs.

   How much money did Jose earn doing odd jobs? _____

Complete the table.

341–342

Regular polygon	Number of sides	Sum of interior angles	Interior angle measure
7. Triangle	3	180°	60°
8. Quadrilateral			
9. Pentagon		540°	108°
10. Hexagon			
11. Heptagon			
12. Octagon		1080°	

DRAW

WRITE

_____
_____
_____
_____
_____
_____
_____
_____

GLOSSARY TO GO

Vocabulary

334, 345

Define each term in your glossary. Draw a picture or give an example of each term.

- Supplementary angles

  Draw two angles that are supplementary and two that are not.

- Polygon

HOME CONNECTION

Game

491

Try this game with a friend. Have your friend—

1. Pick a number.
2. Multiply that number by 10.
3. Add 4 to the product.
4. Divide that sum by 2.

5. Multiply the quotient by 4.
6. Subtract 3 from the product.
7. Divide the difference by 5.

Have your friend tell you what the number is now. Take the number your friend gives you, mentally subtract 1, and divide by 4. The result is the number your friend picked at the beginning!

For example, say the number your friend picks is 12.

$12 \times 10 = 120$; $120 + 4 = 124$; $124 \div 2 = 62$; $62 \times 4 = 248$; $248 - 3 = 245$; $245 \div 5 = 49$

Mentally, $49 - 1 = 48$; $48 \div 4 = 12$!

Try this several times to see if it works with any number your friend picks.

Staying Sharp

Solve these problems on your own.

- The first song on a CD is $4\frac{1}{2}$ minutes long. The second song is $3\frac{5}{6}$ minutes long. How many minutes are both songs together? Give the answer in simplest form. _____

104–107

- How much longer is the first song than the second? _____

132–135

- There are 12 songs on the CD. If the average or mean time of each song is $4\frac{1}{6}$ minutes, how many minutes of music are on the CD? _____

160–163

Write About It

466

- Repeat the fraction experiment from yesterday. What fraction occurred most often this time?

Percent Sense

◆ MATERIALS

Percent Sense Game Board cardstock; Counters cardstock,
10 of each color; two paper clips

◆ DIRECTIONS

1. Players decide who will use green and who will use orange counters.

2. Players sit with the game board between them. Player 1 places the paper clips on two digits at the bottom of the game board, forms a fraction with the selected digits, and places one of his or her counters on the game board on the percent equivalent to this fraction.

3. Player 2 then selects ONE of the paper clips to move to another digit and forms a new fraction, placing one of her or his counters on any free space on the game board containing an equivalent percent.

4. Players continue alternating turns. If a player forms a fraction for which there is no free space on the game board, that player loses the turn.

5. The winner is the first player to have four counters in a row.

PRACTICE

Today's Number:

$\frac{7}{8}$

Name _____

028 Shade each model to show $\frac{7}{8}$.

1.

2. ○○○○○○○○
   ○○○○○○○○
   ○○○○○○○○

3. ○○○○
   ○○○○
   ○○○○

044, 442 Write $\frac{7}{8}$ two different ways.

4. As a decimal. _____

5. As a percent. _____

102, 131 Write each missing number.

6. $4.50 + _____ = $10.00

7. $2.50 + $1.35 + _____ = $5.00

Solve each problem.

161 8. A sweatshirt is on sale for $\frac{7}{8}$ of the regular price. If the regular price is $56, what is the price of the sweatshirt on sale? _____

102, 131 9. Sam bought a CD, juice, and a pretzel. The juice cost $0.85. The pretzel cost $0.75. He spent $16.59 altogether. How much did the CD cost? _____

131 10. A CD costs $17.50 at one store and $14.95 at another store. How much more does the CD cost at the first store? _____

DRAW

WRITE

_____
_____
_____
_____
_____
_____
_____
_____

MAKE & TAKE

GLOSSARY TO GO

Vocabulary

345, 474

Define each term in your glossary. Draw a picture or give an example of each term.

- Concave polygon
- Convex polygon

Define each prefix in your glossary. Give an example of a word with each prefix.

- cent-

  Example

- milli-

  Example

- kilo-

  Example

HOME CONNECTION

Game

491

Review the number trick from yesterday. Has anyone figured out why it works? Try using diagrams or models to show why it works.

If your friends are not tired of your tricks yet, try this one.

1. Think of a number.
2. Multiply it by 10.
3. Add 10 to the product.
4. Divide the sum by 2.
5. Add 5 to the quotient.
6. Divide the sum by 5.

Have your friend tell you what the number is now. Take the number your friend gives you and subtract 2. The result is the number your friend picked at the beginning!

See if you and your friends can figure out why this number trick works. Pictures or symbols may help.

Staying Sharp

442

Solve this problem on your own.

What percent of the large square is each lettered section?

A _____ , B _____ , C _____ , D _____

Shade each model to show $\frac{9}{10}$.

1.

2. ○○○○○○○○○○
○○○○○○○○○○
○○○○○○○○○○

3. ○○○○○
○○○○○
○○○○○
○○○○○
○○○○○

028

Write $\frac{9}{10}$ two different ways.

4. As a decimal. _____

5. As a percent. _____

044, 442

Use mental math to find each answer.

6. $\frac{9}{10}$ of $2.00 _____

7. $\frac{9}{10}$ of $25.00 _____

8. $\frac{9}{10}$ of $7.00 _____

143–148

Use a pattern to complete the table.

067–069

1	9
2	18
9.	27
10. 5	
11. 10	
12.	108
13.	279

DRAW

WRITE

_____
_____
_____
_____
_____
_____
_____
_____

Weekly Newsletter

Each day your child will be bringing home material that reviews and extends math concepts studied in class. These will include problems for your child to solve alone and games or other activities that will allow you to help your child explore mathematical concepts.

In the second week of the Summer Success Math program, your child continued to learn and practice math concepts such as fractions, decimals, and percents, ratios, proportions, and attributes of various two-dimensional shapes. The Glossary your child is compiling reflects these concepts. Here is a list of math terms we defined this week.

- interior, exterior, and supplementary angles
- polygon, concave and convex polygons
- regular figures, similar figures
- common math prefixes such as *cent-*, *milli-*, and *kilo-*

This week your child used fractions to compare prices, solving problems comparing sale and regular prices, or determining which store is offering the better deal. We have emphasized solving problems like these mentally, since figuring these things out with paper and pencil in a store is usually not possible. This kind of math will be useful to your child throughout his or her life.

We also worked on developing a better understanding of the relative size of fractions by comparing them to one whole and common fractions such as $\frac{1}{2}$. Fractional parts of models and groups of items were used to reinforce these comparisons. For example, we compared shading $\frac{2}{3}$, or 8, of 12 rectangles with shading $\frac{3}{4}$, or 9, of 12 rectangles to see that the difference between the two amounts is $\frac{1}{12}$. We also added and subtracted fractions.

We studied the angles of two-dimensional shapes and learned to figure out the size of the angles in regular shapes such as triangles and hexagons.

Some of the material your child will work on is homework. Parents often ask how they can help children with homework, especially when it starts to get more complicated. If you are good at math, be careful not to take over the homework. Try not to show your child **how** to solve a problem. Help your child **figure out how** to solve the problem. If you are not that good at math, don't worry. There are still many ways to help. Here are some questions you might try asking.

- What is the problem you're working on?
- What did the teacher tell you to do, or what do the directions say?
- What do you understand about the problem? What don't you understand?
- Are there any words or directions that you are uncertain about?
- Where do you think you should begin?
- What do you already know that can help you work through the problem?
- Can you draw a picture or make a table to help you?

No matter how much or how little math you know, remember that words of encouragement and support will go a long way toward helping your child develop confidence in her or his ability to solve math problems. Don't forget to point out math in the real world whenever you see it. This week, showing your child ads for sales in stores will be a big help.

PRACTICE

Today's Number: ⁻1

Name_____

Answer each question.

1. What is the opposite of ⁺1? _____

2. On the x-axis, is ⁻1 to the left or the right of zero? _____

3. On the y-axis, is ⁻1 above or below zero? _____

4. What is ⁺1 + ⁻1? _____

Show ⁻1 + ⁻1 + ⁻1 on the number line.

5.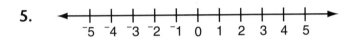

Write an addition equation for the positive (p) and negative (n) counters.

6. (p)(n)(n) _____

7. (p)(p)(n)(n) _____

Write the missing numbers.

8. ⁺1 + _____ = ⁺2

9. ⁺1 + _____ = 0

10. ⁻1 + _____ = 0

11. ⁻1 + _____ = ⁻2

DRAW

WRITE

MAKE & TAKE

046–047

GLOSSARY TO GO

Vocabulary

Define each term in your glossary. Draw a picture or give an example of each term.

• Integers

HOME CONNECTION

318–320

Staying Sharp

Locate these points on this coordinate grid. Connect the points with straight lines in the order they are listed. Describe what you see. (2, ⁻3), (2, ⁻7), (9, ⁻7), (9, 6), (8, 6), (8, 5), (7, 5), (7, 10), (9, 9), (7, 8), (7, 6), (6, 6), (6, 5), (5, 5), (5, 6), (4, 6), (4, 1), (2, 1), (2, 4), (1, 3), (0, 4), (⁻1, 3), (⁻2, 4), (⁻2, 1), (⁻4, 1), (⁻4, 6), (⁻5, 6), (⁻5, 5), (⁻6, 5), (⁻6, 6), (⁻7, 6), (⁻7, 10), (⁻9, 9), (⁻7, 8), (⁻7, 5), (⁻8, 5), (⁻8, 6), (⁻9, 6), (⁻9, ⁻7), (⁻2, ⁻7), (⁻2, ⁻3), (2, ⁻3)

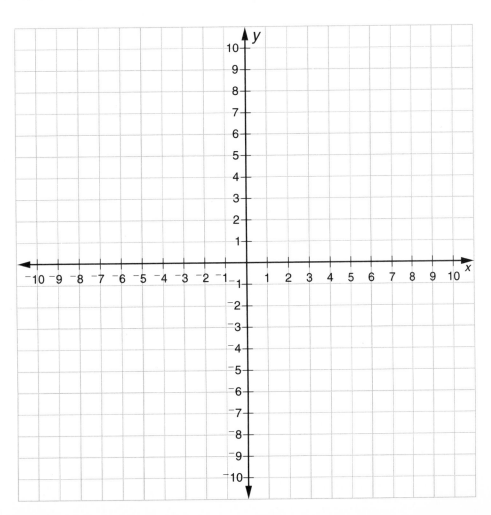

Pick an Integer

◆ **MATERIALS**

Pick an Integer Game Board cardstock; 1 sheet Counters cardstock; Integer Cards cardstock (26 cards); paper bag

◆ **DIRECTIONS**

1. Players decide who will use green and who will use orange counters. Place the separated Integer Cards in the paper bag.

2. Players sit with the game board between them. Player 1 draws two Integer Cards from the bag and uses them as coordinates of a point on the game board grid. The player determines which will be the *x*- and *y*-coordinate. For example, if 5 and ⁻3 are drawn, the player may choose (5, ⁻3) or (⁻3, 5). Player 1 places a counter on the selected point and returns the Integer Cards to the bag.

3. Player 2 repeats the same steps.

4. Once a point is covered, it may not be covered again. If both possible points are covered, the player loses the turn.

5. The winner is the first player to cover three points in a row, either vertically, horizontally, or diagonally.

Answer each question.

046

1. What is the opposite of $^+2$? _____

318

2. On the *x*-axis, is $^-2$ to the right or the left of zero? _____

3. On the *y*-axis, is $^-2$ above or below zero? _____

108

4. What is $^+2 + ^-2$? _____

5. Show $^-2 + ^-2 + ^-2$ on the number line.

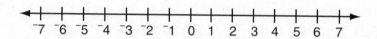

108

Write an addition equation for the positive ⓟ and negative ⓝ counters.

6. ⓟ ⓟ ⓝ ⓝ _____

108

Write the missing numbers.

7. $^+2 +$ _____ $= ^+4$ 8. $^-2 +$ _____ $= 0$ 9. $^-2 +$ _____ $= ^-4$

048

Compare the numbers. Write < or >.

10. $^-2$ _____ $^-1$ 11. 0 _____ $^-2$ 12. $^-2$ _____ $^-4$

13. 3 _____ $^-4$ 14. $^-3$ _____ $^-4$ 15. 3 _____ 4

DRAW

WRITE

_____

_____

_____

_____

_____

_____

_____

_____

Glossary to Go

Vocabulary

Define each term in your glossary. Draw a picture or give an example of each term.

- Parallelogram
- Trapezoid

Home Connection

Staying Sharp

Solve these problems on your own.

067, 069

- What number when divided by 2, 3, 4, and 6 has a remainder of 1, but when divided by 7 has no remainder? _____

424

- A recipe for 8 servings of punch calls for $\frac{1}{2}$ can of orange juice concentrate, $2\frac{1}{2}$ cups of lemon-lime soda, $1\frac{1}{2}$ cups of water, and the juice of 1 lemon. If you want to make enough punch to serve 24 people, how much of each ingredient do you need? Use the ratio table to get your answer.

	8 people	16 people	24 people
orange juice concentrate	$\frac{1}{2}$ can		
lemon-lime soda	$2\frac{1}{2}$ cups		
water	$1\frac{1}{2}$ cups		
whole lemon	1		

- Try to solve these problems mentally.

088–091

$\frac{1}{5} + \frac{1}{10} + \frac{2}{3} + \frac{9}{10} + \frac{4}{5} =$ _____

$\frac{1}{2} + \frac{3}{4} + \frac{3}{8} =$ _____

$0.7 + 1.5 + 0.3 + 0.04 =$ _____

143–148

$4 \times \$20.05 =$ _____

173–175

$\$10.40 \div 4 =$ _____

Answer each question.

1. What is ⁺3 + ⁻3? _____

108

Show ⁻3 + ⁺3 + ⁻3 on the number line.

108

2.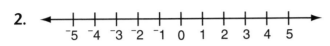
⁻5 ⁻4 ⁻3 ⁻2 ⁻1 0 1 2 3 4 5

Draw positive ⓟ and negative ⓝ counters to show ⁻3 − ⁺2 = ⁻5.

136

3.

Write each product.

164

4. ⁺3 × ⁻3 = _____   5. ⁻3 × ⁻3 = _____   6. ⁻3 × ⁺30 = _____

Find a pattern and complete the table.

164

1	⁻3
2	⁻6
⁻1	3
7.	9
8. 5	
9.	36

Solve the problem.

366, 158–159

10. What is the area of a square that has a side length of 3.3 cm?

_____

DRAW

WRITE

_____

_____

_____

_____

_____

_____

_____

_____

MAKE & TAKE

GLOSSARY TO GO

Vocabulary

Define each term in your glossary. Draw a picture or give an example of each term.

- Coordinate grid
- *x*-axis
- *y*-axis
- Ordered pair
- Origin

HOME CONNECTION

Staying Sharp

Draw a design on this coordinate grid using only straight lines. Each line must connect two points on the grid. The design must use all four quadrants of the grid. Write all the ordered pairs you use to the right of the grid.

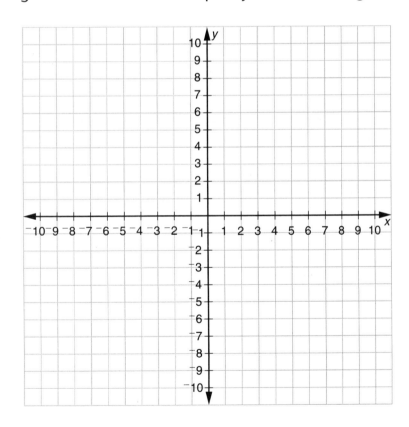

Find the Alien Space Ships

◆ MATERIALS

Find the Alien Space Ships Pieces cardstock, paper, pencils

◆ DIRECTIONS

1. The object of the game is to find all three of the other player's space ships.

2. Each player uses one coordinate grid and three same-colored Space Ships. Players sit across from each other with their grids in front of them. A tall book or other divider should be placed between the players to prevent them seeing the other player's grid.

3. Each player places the three space ships on his or her grid. All four corners of each space ship must appear at a point that can be named with an ordered pair.

4. In each turn, one player names an ordered pair. The other player tells the first player how that point relates to a specific space ship. The point may be hidden by a space ship. The point may define one of the four corners of a space ship. The point may be close to or far from a corner of a space ship. For example, suppose Space Ship 2 is located with the corners at ($^-6$, 3), ($^-2$, 3), ($^-2$, $^-1$), and ($^-6$, $^-1$). If the other player names ($^-1$, 3), a good response would be, "That point is very close to Space Ship 2."

5. Players should write down the information they receive in each turn so they can narrow down the location of each space ship.

6. Players alternate turns asking questions and giving clues. Play continues until one player can correctly name the ordered pair for each corner of all three of the other player's space ships.

Today's Number: ⁻5

Name _____

Answer each question.

046

1. What is the opposite of ⁺5? _____

318

2. On the *y*-axis, is ⁻5 below or above zero? _____

3. On the *x*-axis, is ⁺5 to the right or the left of zero? _____

136, 164 **Write the missing numbers.**

4. $^{+}5 - {}^{-}5 =$ _____   5. $^{+}5 \times {}^{-}5 =$ _____   6. $^{-}5 \times {}^{-}5 =$ _____

164 **Complete the multiplication table.**

×	⁻4	⁻3	⁻2	⁻1	1	2	3	4
5	⁻20					10		
4	⁻16							
3	⁻12	⁻9	⁻6	⁻3	3	6	9	12
2	⁻8		⁻4					
1	⁻4					2		
0	0							
⁻1	4				⁻1	⁻2		
⁻2	8							
⁻3	12					⁻6	⁻9	
⁻4	16							⁻16
⁻5	20					⁻10		

DRAW

WRITE

_____
_____
_____
_____
_____
_____
_____

MAKE & TAKE

291–296

GLOSSARY TO GO

◀ Vocabulary

Define each term in your glossary. Draw a picture or give an example of each term.

• Histogram

HOME CONNECTION

108, 136

◀ Game

Play this game with a friend or family member. You will need to make a set of 26 Integer Cards. Use 3" × 5" index cards if they are available. With a red pen or marker, make 10 cards with positive numbers from $^+1$ to $^+10$. Then make 3 more red cards all marked $^+10$. With a black pen or marker, make 10 cards with negative numbers from $^-1$ to $^-10$. Then make 3 more black cards all marked $^-10$.

Directions

1. Shuffle the Integer Cards well and put them in a facedown stack between the players. Each player draws seven cards.

2. Players take turns trying to make equations that equal zero. For example, if a player has $^-3$, $^-7$, $^-10$, $^-10$, $^+2$, $^+10$, $^+10$, one possible equation is $^+10 + {}^+10 + {}^-3 + {}^-7 + {}^-10 = 0$. All cards used in the equations must be displayed faceup so the equations can be checked. Players must read their equations aloud. All cards used in the equation are then placed facedown in a discard pile.

3. If a player is unable to make an equation equaling 0, he or she draws cards from the facedown stack until an equation for 0 can be made.

4. The winner is the first player to run out of cards. If all cards in the facedown stack have been used and neither player is out of cards, shuffle the cards in the discard pile and keep playing until one player is out of cards.

046

Answer each question.

1. What is the opposite of $^+10$? _____

108, 136, 164, 193

Write the missing numbers.

2. $^+10 + {}^-10 =$ _____

3. $^+10 - {}^-10 =$ _____

4. $^-10 +$ _____ $= {}^-15$

5. $^-10 \times {}^-5 =$ _____

6. $^+10 \times {}^-10 =$ _____

7. _____ $\times {}^-10 = {}^-20$

8. $^+10 \div {}^-10 =$ _____

9. $^-10 \div$ _____ $= 2$

10. $^-1000 \div {}^-10 =$ _____

11. $^+100 \div$ _____ $= {}^-50$

164

Write each product.

12. $^-10 \times {}^-10 \times {}^-10 =$ _____

13. $^-10 \times {}^+10 \times {}^-10 \times {}^+10 =$ _____

368

Solve the problem.

14. What is the area of the trapezoid? Use the formula $A = \frac{1}{2}h(b_1 + b_2)$.

_____

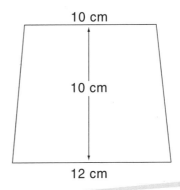

10 cm

10 cm

12 cm

DRAW

WRITE

_____
_____
_____
_____
_____
_____
_____
_____

Weekly Newsletter

Each day your child will be bringing home material that reviews and extends math concepts studied in class. These will include problems for your child to solve alone and games or other activities that will allow you to help your child explore mathematical concepts.

The math concepts we studied this week are reflected in the definitions your child has added to his or her Glossary.

- integers
- parallelogram, trapezoid
- coordinate grid, x- and y-axes, ordered pair, origin
- histogram

This week your child studied integers, or positive and negative whole numbers. These numbers are used in algebra and in much of the math your child will study in high school and beyond. We use negative numbers in daily life as well. For example, to describe the temperature if it is one degree below zero we say minus one or negative 1. If a football team moves forward we say plus yards. If it loses yards, we say minus yards. If you add up the plus and minus yards you will find out whether the team moved forward or backward over all.

Integers are used to represent opposites. The opposite of 1 is -1. The opposite of moving 2 spaces to the right is moving 2 spaces to the left. Losing 3 of something can be represented with a -3; gaining 3 can be represented with a $+3$. Integers can show opposites for right, up, and gain. They tell us what direction to move on a number line.

To demonstrate adding and subtracting integers, we used black (positive) and white (negative) circles. If a black circle is plus one degree of heat and a white circle is minus one degree of heat, what happens when you add the two? The result is zero. Ask your child to show you how these black and white circles work.

We also learned a game this week that features integers. Ask your child to explain how to play the game. Directions for a similar game have been brought home this week. Try to take time to play the game with your child.

Your child also used the coordinate grid this week. Like a map with letters and numbers to identify a specific place, the coordinate grid uses numbers, positive and negative, to identify every point on the grid. In future weeks, your child will use this grid to determine area, draw reflections, compare data, and so on.

Take a look at the homework your child brings home each day. Try to stay involved with your child's progress when you can. Remember to point out math in the real world, wherever you find it.

Answer each question.

1. What are the factors of 12? _____   `056`

2. What are the factors of 20? _____

3. What are the common factors of 12 and 20? _____   `065`

4. What is the prime factorization of 12? _____   `061`

5. What is the prime factorization of 20? _____

6. What are the first six multiples of 12? _____   `067, 068`

7. What are two common multiples of 12 and 20? _____

8. What is $\frac{1}{12} + \frac{1}{20}$? _____   `107`

Solve each problem.

9. How many eggs are in $\frac{1}{3}$ of a dozen? _____   `032`

10. How many inches are in $\frac{1}{6}$ of a foot? _____

11. How many inches are in $2\frac{1}{2}$ feet? _____

12. Which number does not belong   `067`
    in the pattern 4, 8, 12, 16, 18, 20? _____

13. What is the area of this triangle? Show your work.   `356`

$2\frac{1}{2}$ cm

12 cm

DRAW

WRITE

_____

_____

_____

_____

_____

_____

_____

_____

MAKE & TAKE

Vocabulary

Define each term in your glossary. Draw a picture or give an example of each term.

• Factor

• Multiple

• Prime number

056,
067, 058

HOME CONNECTION

Staying Sharp

• Fill in the table.

Number	Factors	Sum of factors other than the number
2	1, 2	1
3	1, 3	1
4	1, 2, 4	3
5		
6		
7		
8		
9	1, 3, 9	4
10		
11		
12		
13		
14		
15		
16		
17		
18		21
19		
20		
21		

• What patterns do you see?

The Factor Game

♦ MATERIALS

One 1–6 number cube, one 4–9 number cube

♦ DIRECTIONS

1. Players make a copy of the recording sheet.

2. Player 1 rolls both number cubes, uses the digits to make a two-digit number, and receives points equal to that number. Player 2 receives points equal to the sum of all the factors of that number, except one and the number itself. For example, if 2 and 7 are rolled, the numbers 27 and 72 can be made. If 27 is made, Player 1 gets 27 points and Player 2 gets 12 points. If the number 72 is made, Player 1 gets 72 points and Player 2 gets 122 points. Players record their points after each turn on the recording sheet.

3. To continue, Player 2 rolls both number cubes. The player who rolls always receives points equal to the two-digit number; the other player receives points equal to the sum of all the factors of that number, except one and the number itself.

4. Play alternates back and forth until five rounds have been played.

5. Players add their points from all five rounds. The player with more points is the winner.

The Factor Game

Round		Player 1 _____	Player 2 _____
1	Number rolled	27	
	Sum of Factors		12
	Number rolled		49
	Sum of Factors	7	
2	Number rolled		
	Sum of Factors		
	Number rolled		
	Sum of Factors		
3	Number rolled		
	Sum of Factors		
	Number rolled		
	Sum of Factors		

Answer each question.

056   1. What are the factors of 24? _____

061   2. What is the prime factorization of 24? _____

Solve each problem.

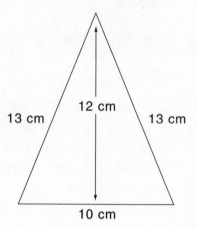

032   3. How many eggs are in $\frac{1}{3}$ of two dozen? _____

   4. How many eggs are in $\frac{5}{12}$ of two dozen? _____

   5. How many eggs are in $\frac{3}{4}$ of two dozen? _____

067   6. Which number does not belong
      in the pattern 6, 12, 18, 22, 30, 36? _____

356   7. What is the area of this triangle? Show your work.

13 cm   12 cm   13 cm

10 cm

549   **Use the drawing to answer question 8.**

   8. How many squares will be in
      the 20th design in this pattern?
      Show your work.

1

2   3   4

DRAW

WRITE

_____

_____

_____

_____

_____

_____

_____

_____

GLOSSARY TO GO

Vocabulary

Define each term in your glossary. Draw a picture or give an example of each term.

• Prime factorization

HOME CONNECTION

Staying Sharp

Solve these problems on your own.

• Milk, bread, and peanut butter cost $7.83.
The milk costs $1.99 and the bread costs $1.89.
How much does the peanut butter cost? _____

• The refreshments for a party cost $12.65.
If five friends split the cost, how much does
each friend have to pay? _____

• A pair of $40 shoes are on sale for 10% off.
How much do they cost on sale? _____

• One CD costs $13.99. What is the cost of 11 CDs? _____

• If you save 15¢ every day in a jar, how much will you save

—in the month of February in leap year? _____

—in the month of August? _____

—in one year (not a leap year)? _____

061

131

184

442

158

158

Name_____

Answer each question.

1. What are the factors of 36? _____   `056`

2. What is the prime factorization of 36? _____   `061`

Solve each problem.

3. How many inches are in $\frac{1}{6}$ of a yard? _____

4. How many inches are in $\frac{5}{6}$ of a yard? _____

5. How many inches are in $\frac{2}{9}$ of a yard? _____

6. What is the area of this triangle? Show your work.   `356`

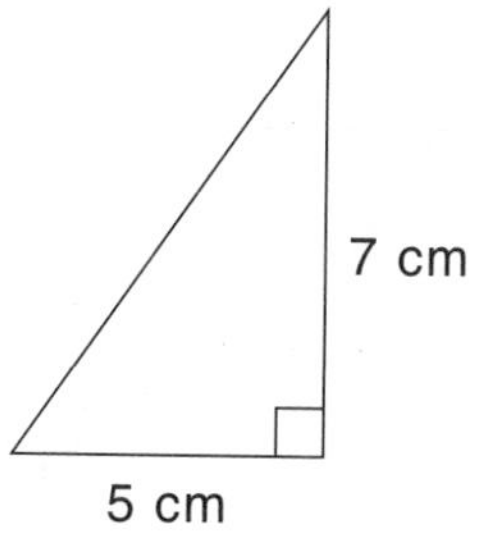

7 cm

5 cm

Use the drawing to answer questions 7 and 8.   `549`

7. How many circles are in the
   next figure in the pattern? _____

8. How many circles are in the 6th figure
   in the pattern? Show your work.

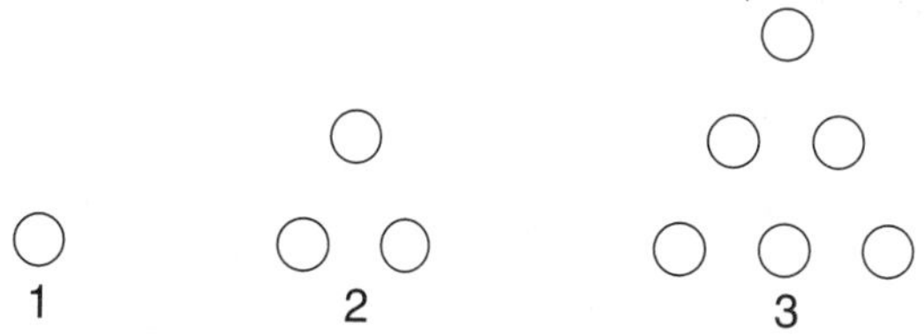

1   2   3

DRAW

WRITE

_____
_____
_____
_____
_____
_____
_____

MAKE & TAKE

GLOSSARY TO GO

Vocabulary

Define each term in your glossary. Draw a picture or give an example of each term.

• Least common multiple (LCM)

HOME CONNECTION

• Fill in the table.

Number	Factors	Sum of factors other than the number
22	1, 2, 11, 22	14
23	1, 23	1
24		36
25		
26		
27		
28		
29	1, 29	1
30		
31		
32		
33		
34		
35		
36		
37		
38		22
39		
40		
41		

• What are the prime numbers between 1 and 41? _____

_____

• Which number between 1 and 41 has the largest number of factors? _____

Grade 7   **73**

I Am... Who Is?

◆ **MATERIALS**

I Am... Who Is? Cards cardstock (15 cards)

◆ **DIRECTIONS**

1. Players shuffle and deal out the cards until only one remains. That card is turned faceup to begin play.

2. The dealer reads the statement and question on the faceup card. The player who has the card with the answer to the first card places it faceup, reading the statement and question on the new card.

3. The player who has the card with the answer continues in the same way.

4. Play continues until one player runs out of cards. That player is the winner.

Today's Number: **60**

Name _____

Answer each question.

056

1. What are the factors of 60? _____

061

2. What is the prime factorization of 60? _____

Solve each problem.

032,
442–445

3. What is $\frac{1}{4}$ of 60? _____

4. What fraction of 60 is 12? _____

5. What percent of 60 is 12? _____

6. What percent of 60 is 20? _____

7. What is 125% of 60? _____

8. What percent of 60 is 45? _____

356

9. What is the area of this triangle? Show your work.

9 in.

7 in.

549

Use the drawing to answer question 10.

10. How many circles are in the 200th figure in the pattern?

1

2

3

DRAW

WRITE

_____
_____
_____
_____
_____
_____
_____

MAKE & TAKE

◆ GLOSSARY TO GO

◆ Vocabulary

Define each term in your glossary. Draw a picture or give an example of each term.

- Greatest common factor (GCF)
- Scalene triangle
- Isosceles triangle
- Equilateral triangle

◆ HOME CONNECTION

◆ Staying Sharp

Practice these math problems with a friend or family member. If possible, have someone test you to see how quickly you can answer them. Try them several times.

What is your best time?

$7 \times 7 =$ _____

$8 \times 9 =$ _____

$9 \times 6 =$ _____

$81 \div 9 =$ _____

$56 \div 7 =$ _____

$64 \div 8 =$ _____

$10 \times 17 =$ _____

$10 \times 170 =$ _____

$100 \times 1700 =$ _____

$5200 \div 10 =$ _____

$60,060 \div 10 =$ _____

$450 \div 100 =$ _____

Answer each question.

1. What are the factors of 72? _____ 056

2. What is the prime factorization of 72? _____ 061

Solve each problem.

3. What is $\frac{1}{4}$ of 72? _____   4. What fraction of 72 is 12? _____ 032, 442–445

5. What percent of 72 is 12? _____   6. What percent of 72 is 24? _____

7. What is 125% of 72? _____   8. What percent of 72 is 48? _____

9. What is the area of one of the triangles formed by one   345, 356
   of the diagonals of this figure? Show your work.

5 cm

Use the drawing to answer questions 10 and 11.   316, 321

10. How many lines
    connect 5 points? _____

11. How many lines
    connect 7 points? _____

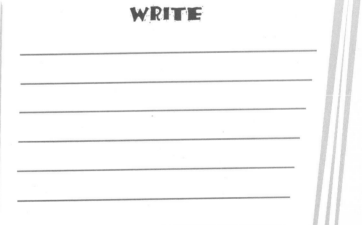

DRAW   **WRITE**

_____

_____

_____

_____

_____

_____

_____

Weekly Newsletter

Each day your child will be bringing home material that reviews and extends math concepts studied in class. These will include problems for your child to solve alone and games or other activities that will allow you to help your child explore mathematical concepts.

The math concepts we studied this week are reflected in the definitions your child has added to his or her Glossary.

- factor, multiple, prime number
- prime factorization
- least common multiple, greatest common factor
- scalene, isosceles, and equilateral triangles

This week your child studied factors and multiples. These concepts make it easier to solve more math problems mentally. The concepts are also important when solving problems with fractions and ratios. Ask your child to tell you what factors and multiples are. Most importantly, ask him or her to explain the **difference** between a factor and a multiple. For example, ask your child to tell you the factors of 12, and some multiples of 12.

Your child's homework this week involved completing tables of factors and their sums for all the numbers from 2 to 41. Take a look at these tables with your child. In addition to any patterns he or she mentions, add any patterns you see in the tables.

Work at home this week also involved more math problems normally encountered in stores. Add problems you discover in newspaper ads or circulars to keep your child's mental math skills sharp.

We also began solving more complicated algebra problems this week. We began by looking for patterns. Once a pattern has been discovered, it is possible to use what is known to predict with certainty what future terms of the pattern will be. Later we learned to substitute known quantities to determine the value of two variables. We used pictures to develop some informal strategies for solving systems of equations. Ask your child to share some of the problems with you.

Look for examples of scalene, isosceles, and equilateral triangles in the world around you. Share them with your child and ask him or her to describe the triangles you find.

Encourage your child to share one new thing with you that he or she learned this week.

Remember to point out math in the real world, wherever you find it.

Write the value of each expression.

071

1. 2^2 _____

2. 5^2 _____

3. 10^2 _____

4. 6^2 _____

5. 9^2 _____

6. 15^2 _____

Write each value of n.

076

7. For $n^2 = 9$, $n =$ _____

8. For $n^2 = 64$, $n =$ _____

9. For $n^2 = 121$, $n =$ _____

Use the drawing to answer questions 10–13.

394

10. How many faces? _____

11. How many vertices? _____

12. How many edges? _____

13. Each face is the shape of what polygon? _____

Solve the problem.

491

14. Since $25^2 = 625$, what is 24×26? _____

Use the drawing to answer questions 15 and 16.

229

15. One apple weighs as much as how many bananas? _____

16. One banana weighs as much as how many apples? _____

DRAW

WRITE

_____

_____

_____

_____

_____

_____

_____

_____

MAKE & TAKE

GLOSSARY TO GO

Vocabulary

Define each term in your glossary. Draw a picture or give an example of each term.

- Face
- Vertex (vertices)
- Edge

HOME CONNECTION

Staying Sharp

- Fill in the table.

Number (n)	Number squared (n^2)
2	4
3	
4	
5	
6	
7	
8	
9	
10	
11	
12	
13	
14	
15	
16	

- Put a check mark next to the squares you know by heart. Memorize one new one tonight. Do you think you could learn all the squares from 1 to 20 this summer?

Game

Play this game with a friend or family member. See if you can figure out a good winning strategy.

Directions

Game of 21.

1. Players take turns counting to 21. Players can count by one or by two. For example, if the first player says 1, 2, the next player can say either 3, or 3, 4.

2. The player who says 21 wins.

The Numbers of NIM

◆ MATERIALS

12 Counters cardstock

◆ DIRECTIONS

1. Arrange the 12 counters in three rows with three counters in the top row, four in the middle row, and five in the bottom row.

2. Player 1 removes any number of counters from any single row. Counters may not be removed from more than one row. For example, removing four counters from the bottom row is allowed, but removing two counters from the bottom row and two from the middle row is not allowed.

3. Player 2 removes any number of counters from any single row.

4. Players alternate turns. The player who removes the last of the 12 counters wins.

071 Write the value of each expression.

1. 2^3 _____   2. 3^3 _____   3. 10^3 _____

4. 1^3 _____   5. 5^3 _____   6. 9^3 _____

080 Write each value of n.

7. For $n^3 = 64$, $n =$ _____   8. For $n^3 = 1$, $n =$ _____   9. For $n^3 = 125$, $n =$ _____

399–401 Use the drawing of the cube to answer questions 10–14.

10. How many faces? _____

11. How many vertices? _____

12. How many edges? _____

13. Each face is the shape of what polygon? _____

14. What is the surface area of the cube? _____

2 cm

229 Use the drawing to answer questions 15 and 16.

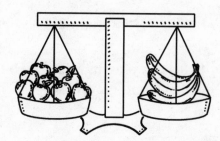

15. One banana weighs as much as how many apples? _____

16. One apple weighs as much as how many bananas? _____

DRAW

WRITE

_____
_____
_____
_____
_____
_____
_____
_____

GLOSSARY TO GO

Vocabulary

Define each term in your glossary. Draw a picture or give an example of each term.

- Polyhedron
- Prism
- Base of a prism
- Surface area

394, 396

HOME CONNECTION

Staying Sharp

Solve these problems on your own.

- Write a fraction to describe the shaded part of each set of triangles. Write it in simplest form.

028, 037

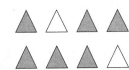

_____   _____

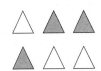

_____   _____

- Write each of these fractions as a percent. Draw a picture of one of them.

044, 026

$\frac{3}{4}$ _____

$\frac{2}{3}$ _____

$\frac{1}{8}$ _____

$\frac{7}{8}$ _____

$\frac{1}{6}$ _____

$\frac{5}{6}$ _____

PRACTICE

Today's Number: 3^3

Name_____

Write the value of each expression.

1. 3^3 _____

2. 4^3 _____

3. 10^3 _____

4. 6^3 _____

5. 1^3 _____

6. 100^3 _____

Use the drawing to answer questions 7–9.

7. How many faces? _____

8. What is the surface area of the cube? _____

9. What is the volume of the cube? _____

3 cm

Solve the problem.

10. On Monday you received $3.00. On Tuesday you received three times as much money. On Wednesday you received three times the amount that you received on Tuesday. How much money did you receive altogether?

_____

Use the drawing to answer questions 11–13.

11. Which is heavier, an apple or a banana? _____

12. One banana weighs as much as how many apples? _____

13. One apple weighs as much as how many bananas? _____

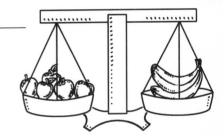

DRAW

WRITE

_____
_____
_____
_____
_____
_____
_____
_____

© Great Source. Permission is granted to copy this page.

MAKE & TAKE

GLOSSARY TO GO

Vocabulary

Define each term in your glossary. Draw a picture or give an example of each term.

- Exponent
- Base of an exponent

HOME CONNECTION

Staying Sharp

- Fill in the table.

Number (n)	Number squared (n^2)
10	100
11	
12	
13	
14	
15	
16	
17	
18	
19	
20	
100	
1000	

- Put a check mark next to the squares you know by heart. Memorize one new one tonight.

Poison

◆ MATERIALS

19 Counters cardstock, 18 of one color and one counter of a different color

◆ DIRECTIONS

1. The object of the game is to force the other player to take the last, or "Poison," counter.

2. Arrange the 19 counters in a single row with the different-color counter last. That counter is "Poison."

3. Player 1 removes either one or two counters from the beginning of the row. Player 2 then removes either one or two counters from the beginning of the row.

4. Players alternate turns. The player who is forced to remove the "Poison" counter loses.

Write the value of each expression.

071

1. 2^4 _____

2. 1^4 _____

3. 10^4 _____

4. 3^4 _____

5. 4^4 _____

6. 100^4 _____

207–209

7. $2 + 4 \times 5$ _____

8. $(10 - 2) \times (4 + 3)$ _____

9. $4 \div 2 + 2^4$ _____

10. $(10 - 2) \times 4 + 3$ _____

403, 407

Use the drawing to answer questions 11 and 12.

11. What is the name of this figure?

    _____

12. What is the surface area?

    _____

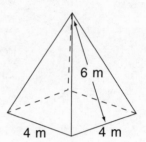

6 m

4 m   4 m

229

Use the drawing to answer questions 13 and 14.

13. Which is heavier,
    an apple or a banana? _____

14. One banana weighs as
    much as how many apples? _____

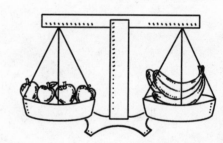

DRAW

WRITE

_____

_____

_____

_____

_____

_____

_____

_____

GLOSSARY TO GO

Vocabulary

Define each term in your glossary. Draw a picture or give an example of each term.

- Pyramid

HOME CONNECTION

044–045,
026, 442

Staying Sharp

- Fill in the table. Look for patterns. Describe one pattern you notice.

Fraction	Decimal	Percent
$\frac{1}{2}$	0.5	50%
$\frac{1}{4}$		
$\frac{1}{8}$		
$\frac{3}{8}$		
$\frac{5}{8}$		
$\frac{3}{4}$		
$\frac{7}{8}$		
$\frac{1}{3}$		
$\frac{1}{6}$		
$\frac{2}{3}$		
$\frac{5}{6}$		
$\frac{1}{5}$		
$\frac{1}{10}$		
$\frac{1}{9}$	0.111. . .	
$\frac{2}{9}$		
$\frac{3}{9}$		
$\frac{4}{9}$		

Write the value of each expression.

1. 10^3 _____

2. 10^4 _____

3. 10^5 _____

4. 10^8 _____

5. $10 \times 10 \div 10$ _____

6. $10 + 10 \times 10 \times 10$ _____

7. $(10 + 10) \times 10 \times 10$ _____

8. $10^3 \times 10^4$ _____

9. $10^3 + 10^4$ _____

10. $10^6 \div 10^3$ _____

071 207–209 006

Use the drawing to answer questions 11–13.
The base is a regular hexagon.

403, 407

11. What is the area of the hexagonal base? _____

12. What is the area of each triangular face? _____

13. What is the surface area? _____

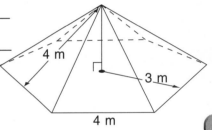

4 m

3 m

4 m

Solve each problem.

229

14. If two apples plus three pounds weigh $4\frac{1}{2}$ pounds,

    how much does one apple weigh? _____

15. If four bananas plus eight pounds weigh 10 pounds,

    how much does one banana weigh? _____

DRAW

WRITE

_____
_____
_____
_____
_____
_____
_____
_____

Weekly Newsletter

Each day your child will be bringing home material that reviews and extends math concepts studied in class. These will include problems for your child to solve alone and games or other activities that will allow you to help your child explore mathematical concepts.

The math concepts we studied this week are reflected in the definitions your child has added to his or her Glossary.

- faces, vertices, and edges in three-dimensional shapes
- polyhedron, prism, pyramid, base of a prism
- surface area
- exponent, base of an exponent

By now your child should be developing some real confidence in math. To succeed in math, students need two important qualities. They must be curious and they must be persistent. Math is not always easy. Like most worthwhile things, once mastered, it opens many doors to opportunity. Encourage your child to persist, even when the job is difficult.

This week your child learned about exponents. An exponent tells us how many times a number is multiplied by itself. This is a short way of writing a long multiplication sentence. Ask your child to write a number in exponent form and to identify the base of the exponent and the exponent.

As part of the homework this week, your child practiced squaring all the numbers from 1 to 20. See how many of these squares your child has memorized. Encourage him or her to add one or two more to memory each day until all of them can be recited.

In algebra, we solved problems involving balance scales. This is because an equation such as $2x + 3 = 11$ is really like a balance. The quantity on the left side of the equation equals the quantity on the right side, so the scale is balanced. When solving an equation, the scale must remain balanced after each step. This simple balance scale is a good visual way for students to think about equations. Ask your child to show you one of the problems we solved using this method.

Three-dimensional shapes took the stage this week. We studied pyramids and prisms and learned how they are alike and different. Your child should be able to draw an example of each for you. Ask him or her to point out faces, vertices, and edges of these figures. Encourage your child to find such shapes as you walk or drive around. Notice how many buildings are rectangular prisms.

Every week we have been studying different types of graphs. As adults, we read graphs almost every day, either in the newspapers or on television. Understanding information displayed in a graph is an essential skill and an important area of math. This week we looked at the Olympic records for running and swimming for the last few years. We wanted to find a pattern that would allow us to predict the winning times in future Olympics. Ask your child to explain what we found out.

When you find a graph in a newspaper or magazine, share it with your child. Discuss the information it contains. Keeping track of data at home, such as how many hours of TV your family watches in a week or the scores of your favorite sports team, will reinforce the math your child has been learning in school.

Write each number in standard form.

016

1. 1.0×10^6 _____

2. 2.0×10^6 _____

3. 2.1×10^6 _____

4. 2.11×10^6 _____

Write each number using a power of ten.

006

5. one million _____

6. 2,400,000 _____

Write the number in word form.

016

7. 2.11×10^6 _____

Write the value of each expression.

207–209

8. $2 + 2^3 \times 2$ _____

9. $2 + 2 \div 2 \times 2 - 2$ _____

10. $(2 + 2^3) \times 2$ _____

11. $(2 + 2) \div (2 - 1)$ _____

Use the drawing to answer questions 12–14. Use 3.14 for π.

372–373

12. What is the length of the diameter? _____

13. What is the circumference in terms of π? _____

14. What is the circumference? _____

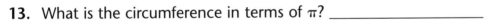

3 units

DRAW

WRITE

_____

_____

_____

_____

_____

_____

_____

_____

_____

MAKE & TAKE

GLOSSARY TO GO

◆ Vocabulary

Define each term in your glossary. Draw a picture or give an example of each term.

- Radius
- Diameter

HOME CONNECTION

◆ Staying Sharp

- Flip a coin 20 times and write down whether heads or tails comes up each time. For example, H, H, T, H, H, and so on. Plot the results on the graph below. Begin at zero on the vertical axis. Number 1 on the horizontal axis represents the first toss, and so on. Move UP one every time heads is flipped and DOWN one every time tails is flipped.

This graph shows how flipping H, H, T, H, H would look.

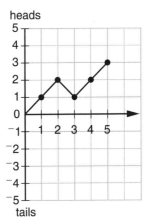

- How many times do you expect the coin to come up heads? How many times do you expect your graph to cross the horizontal axis?

- Use this graph to record your tosses.
- Do you see a pattern?
- How many times did the coin come up heads?
- How many times did your graph cross the horizontal axis?

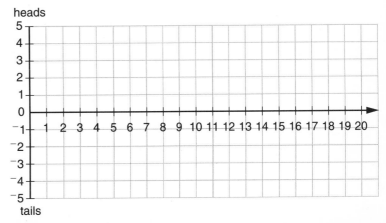

What Are the Odds?

◆ **MATERIALS**

Two 1–6 number cubes, paper, pencil

◆ **DIRECTIONS**

1. Players make a recording sheet like the one shown.

2. Players take turns rolling both number cubes and computing the product of the digits rolled. Player 1 gets a tally mark when the product is odd. Player 2 gets a tally mark when the product is even. The first player to get 10 tally marks wins.

3. In the second round, players switch roles. Player 1 now gets a tally mark when the product is even. Player 2 gets a tally mark when the product is odd. Play the game again.

4. Note who wins each round. Discuss why this may be so. Decide if the game is fair or not. Support your decision with data.

What Are the Odds?

ROUND 1	
Player 1 gets 1 tally mark for each odd product.	**Player 2** gets 1 tally mark for each even product.

The winner is Player _____ .

ROUND 2	
Players switch roles.	
Player 1 gets 1 tally mark for each even product.	**Player 2** gets 1 tally mark for each odd product.

The winner is Player _____ .

Today's Number:

Name _____

1.86 × 10⁵

1.86×10^5

016 Write each number in standard form.

1. 1.86×10^5 _____ 2. 1.234567×10^{10} _____

016 Write each number using scientific notation.

3. The population of the United States is about 280 million. _____

4. Earth is approximately 93,000,000 miles from the sun. _____

5. Light travels about 6,000,000,000,000 miles in one year. _____

016 Write the number in word form.

6. 1.234567×10^{10} _____

_____

Write the value of each expression.

108, 164 7. $2 + {}^-2$ _____

209 9. $3 \times {}^-2$ _____

8. ${}^-2 + {}^-2 + {}^-2$ _____

10. ${}^-2 + 4 \times 5$ _____

Use the drawing to answer questions 11 and 12. Use 3.14 for π.

372 11. What is the length of the radius? _____

375 12. What is the area of the circle? _____

8 in.

DRAW

WRITE

_____
_____
_____
_____
_____
_____
_____
_____

© Great Source. Permission is granted to copy this page.

GLOSSARY TO GO

372–373

Vocabulary

Define each term in your glossary. Draw a picture or give an example of each term.

- Circumference
- Pi (π)

HOME CONNECTION

028, 442

Staying Sharp

Solve these problems on your own.

- Jose wants to read a book with 539 pages in seven days. He wants to read the same number of pages each day. How many pages must he read each day?
- When Jose has read 154 pages, what fraction of the book has he read?
- Maria is reading a book with 360 pages. How many pages has she read when she has read 25% of the book?
- How many pages has she read when she has read about $33\frac{1}{3}$% of the book?

Write each number in scientific notation.

1. 1,234,000 _____

2. 2,500, 000 _____

3. 50,000,000 _____

4. 2,000 × 2,500,000 _____

016

Write each number in standard form and in word form.

5. $1.5 \times 10^6 \times 2.0 \times 10^2$ _____

6. $2.0 \times 10^6 \times 2.0 \times 10^3$ _____

Write the value of each expression.

7. $^-2 \times ^-2$ _____

8. $^-2 \div ^-2$ _____

164, 193

9. $^-2 + ^-2 \times ^-3$ _____

10. $12 \div 3 \times ^-2$ _____

209

Use the drawing to answer questions 11–13. Use 3.14 for π.

11. What is the formula for the surface area

of a cylinder? _____

12. What is the surface area in terms of π?

_____

13. What is the surface area of the cylinder? _____

411–412

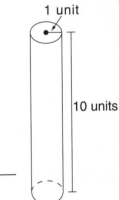

1 unit

10 units

DRAW

WRITE

_____
_____
_____
_____
_____
_____
_____
_____

MAKE & TAKE

◆ HOME CONNECTION

◆ **Staying Sharp**

- Flip two coins 20 times and write down the combinations of heads and tails that appear each time. If possible, use two different kinds of coins such as a nickel and a penny. Use this tally sheet to record the results of your tosses.

TWO HEADS	TWO TAILS	ONE HEAD, ONE TAIL

- Which combination appeared most often—two heads, two tails, or one head and one tail?
- Why do you think that might be so?

Grade 7   **113**

Write each number using scientific notation.

016

1. 6,400,000,000 _____   2. twelve billion _____

3. 2,000 × 6,000,000 _____

4. 3 × 5,880,000,000,000 _____

Write each number in standard form and in word form.

016

5. 5.88×10^{12} _____

6. $2.5 \times 10^4 \times 6.0 \times 10^8$ _____

Write the value of *x* in each equation.

238–242

7. For $2x = 36$, $x =$ _____   8. For $4x = 36$, $x =$ _____

9. For $6x = 36$, $x =$ _____   10. For $8x = 36$, $x =$ _____

Use the drawing to answer questions 11–13.

413, 402

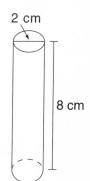

2 cm

8 cm

11. What is the formula for the volume of a cylinder? _____

12. What is the volume of the cylinder?

_____

13. What is the volume of a rectangular prism that would fit exactly

around this cylinder? _____

DRAW

WRITE

_____
_____
_____
_____
_____
_____
_____
_____

MAKE & TAKE

104–107, 132–135

160–163, 187–192

◆ HOME CONNECTION

◆ Staying Sharp

Solve these problems on your own.

$\frac{1}{2} + \frac{1}{4} =$ _____

$1 - \frac{3}{8} =$ _____

$\frac{1}{2} \times \frac{1}{2} =$ _____

$\frac{1}{2} \div \frac{1}{4} =$ _____

$1\frac{1}{2} \div \frac{1}{4} =$ _____

• A costume takes $1\frac{1}{2}$ yards of material to make. You have 15 yards of material. How many costumes can you make?

• How many $\frac{1}{2}$-yard pieces can you make from a 3-yard piece of wood?

Today's Number:

Name _____

1.0×10^{100}

016

Write each product in scientific notation, standard form, and word form.

1. $1.0 \times 10^3 \times 1.0 \times 10^4$ _____

2. $1.0 \times 10^4 \times 1.0 \times 10^4$ _____

3. $1.0 \times 10^5 \times 1.0 \times 10^5$ _____

4. $10,000 \times 100,000$ _____

5. $1,000,000 \times 100,000$ _____

Answer each question.

016

6. What is the number 1.0×10^{100} called? _____

7. How do we say the number 1.0×10^{100} using the word *power*?

_____

Use the drawing to answer questions 8 and 9. Use 3.14 for π.

413

8. What is the volume of the cylinder?

_____

9. If the lengths of the diameter and the height were switched, what would be the volume of the cylinder?

_____

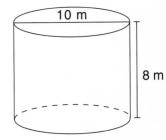

10 m

8 m

DRAW

WRITE

_____

_____

_____

_____

_____

_____

_____

_____

Name _____

Choose or write the best answer for each question.

1. Shade $\frac{5}{6}$ of this set.

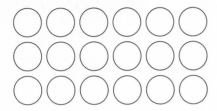

2. Draw a line that is $\frac{7}{8}$ the length of this line.

3. Write the simplest fraction, a decimal, and a percent to show what part of the grid below is shaded.

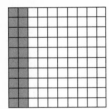

_____ , _____ , _____

4. Write another expression for $2 \times 2 \times 2 \times 2$.

_____

5. Use $<$, $>$, or $=$ to compare the integers.

$^-4$ _____ $^-5$

6. Write $\frac{6}{7}$ as a decimal rounded to the nearest hundredth.

_____

7. Which expression represents 340,000,000 in scientific notation?

(A) 3.4×10^7

(B) 3.4×10^8

(C) 3.4×10^9

(D) 34×10^7

(E) 340×10^6

8. What is the prime factorization of 72?

(A) 7×2 (D) $2^3 \times 3^3$

(B) 8×9 (E) $2^3 \times 3^2$

(C) $2^3 \times 9$

9. What is the value of 8^3?

(A) 24   (D) 83

(B) 64   (E) 512

(C) 72

10. $\frac{7}{12} + \frac{3}{4} =$

(A) $\frac{10}{16}$ (D) $1\frac{1}{4}$

(B) $\frac{5}{8}$ (E) $1\frac{1}{3}$

(C) $\frac{5}{6}$

11. Show $^-2 + \,^-2 + \,^-2$ on the number line.

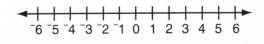

12. What is the value of this expression?
$^-2 + 2 \times 5 - ^-2$

- (A) 0
- (B) 2
- (C) $^-2$
- (D) 10
- (E) 18

13. What is the value of this expression?
$6.0 \times 10^3 \times 3.0 \times 10^5$

- (A) 1.8×10^8
- (B) 1.8×10^9
- (C) 18.0×10^{15}
- (D) 1.8×10^{35}
- (E) Not given

14. $\frac{7}{12}$ of three dozen eggs is how many eggs?

- (A) $1\frac{3}{4}$
- (B) $5\frac{1}{7}$
- (C) 7
- (D) 14
- (E) 21

15. What is the measure of each interior angle of this polygon?

- (A) 30°
- (B) 60°
- (C) 90°
- (D) 120°
- (E) 150°

16. The two triangles below are similar. What is the length of the missing side of the larger triangle?

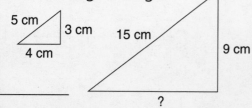

17. Connect the points (2, 2), (4, $^-$2), ($^-$3, $^-$2), and ($^-$2, 2) in order on the grid. What quadrilateral is made?

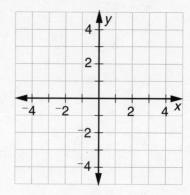

_____

18. Draw a reflection of the figure shown across the *x*-axis. Write the ordered pairs of the new figure.

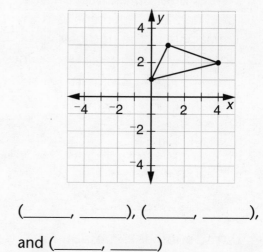

(_____, _____), (_____, _____),

and (_____, _____)

19. Which figure does **not** have 6 rectangular faces?

- (A) rectangular prism
- (B) cube
- (C) rectangular pyramid
- (D) hexagonal prism
- (E) Not given

122   Summer Success: Math

20. What is the circumference of this circle? Use π = 3.14.

(A) 12.56 cm

(B) 25.12 cm

(C) 50.24 cm

(D) 100.48 cm

(E) 200.96 cm

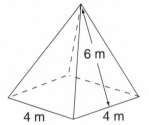

4 cm

21. What is the surface area of this figure?

(A) 16 m²

(B) 28 m²

(C) 64 m²

(D) 96 m²

(E) 112 m²

6 m

4 m   4 m

22. What is the volume of this cylinder? Use π = 3.14.

(A) 60 ft³

(B) 94.2 ft³

(C) 188.4 ft³

(D) 282.6 ft³

(E) 1130.4 ft³

6 ft

10 ft

23. If the pattern continues, what is the area of the 6th figure?

(A) 15 units²

(B) 20 units²

(C) 21 units²

(D) 24 units²

(E) 28 units²

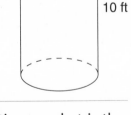

24. Write the next two numbers in this sequence.

$\frac{7}{8}$, $1\frac{3}{4}$, $2\frac{5}{8}$, $3\frac{1}{2}$, _____, _____

25. If $n^3 = 216$, n =

(A) 72   (D) 8

(B) 36   (E) 6

(C) 12

26. In the figure below, one apple weighs as much as how many bananas?

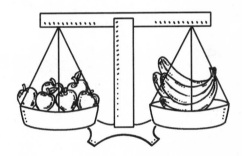

(A) $\frac{2}{3}$ (D) $1\frac{1}{2}$

(B) $\frac{3}{4}$ (E) 2

(C) $1\frac{1}{3}$

27. A store has a 20%-off sale. If the regular price of a pair of jeans is $23, what is the cost of two pairs of jeans on sale?

_____

28. A rectangle has a perimeter of 80 feet. The width is $\frac{1}{3}$ the length. What are the dimensions of the rectangle?

length: _____

width: _____

29. Andy bought 2 notebooks and 2 pens for $3.20. Brad bought 1 notebook and 1 eraser for $1.50. Carrie bought 3 erasers for $0.90. How much did Diana pay for 3 pens? Show your work.

_____

_____

_____

30. What is the probability of spinning either an A or a G on the spinner below?

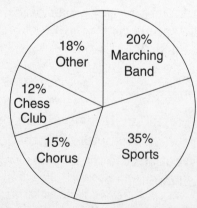

(A) $\frac{1}{8}$

(B) $\frac{1}{4}$

(C) $\frac{1}{16}$

(D) $\frac{1}{32}$

(E) $\frac{1}{64}$

31. The 600 seventh-grade students at Scott Middle School voted to see which after-school activity was their favorite. The results are shown in the graph below. How many students liked sports best?

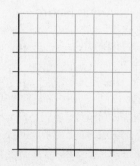

18% Other
20% Marching Band
12% Chess Club
15% Chorus
35% Sports

_____

32. Which statement is true? Use the graph to choose the best answer.

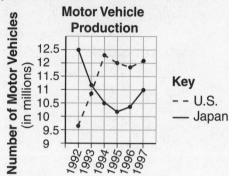

(A) In 1993, both the U.S. and Japan produced about 11 million vehicles.

(B) Vehicle production in the U.S. increased rapidly from 1992 to 1994.

(C) In 1997, about one million more vehicles were made in the U.S. than in Japan.

(D) All of the above

(E) None of the above

33. Make a double-line graph to display the data in the table. Label your graph, give it a title, and include a key.

Average Heights (in centimeters)

Age	12	13	14	15	16
Girls	152	157	160	162	162
Boys	150	157	163	169	174

Each day your child will be bringing home material that reviews and extends math concepts studied in class. These will include problems for your child to solve alone and games or other activities that will allow you to help your child explore mathematical concepts.

The math concepts we studied this week are reflected in the definitions your child has added to his or her Glossary.

- radius, diameter, pi (π)

Your child has been asked to work very hard this summer to learn a lot of math in a short time. Your support and encouragement has been essential. As your child enters eighth grade, your support and encouragement will continue to be important. We sometimes think that math ability is limited to a few people or even that it runs in families. We need to remember that math ability comes from hard work and confidence that the effort will pay off.

This week we studied more concepts that your child will need to know for eighth grade. These included how scientists and mathematicians use a special way of writing large numbers, called scientific notation. For example, the speed of light is 186,000 miles per second. Scientists write this as 1.86×10^5 miles per second. In one year, light travels 5,880,000,000,000, or 5.88×10^{12}, miles. That isn't even one fourth of the distance to the nearest star! You can see why this shorthand way of writing numbers is useful when very large numbers are used frequently.

In geometry we studied the circumference and area of circles, and reviewed the concept of π, which is the ratio of the circumference to the diameter of a circle. The distance around a circle is slightly more than three times the distance across it through the center. This ratio has been studied for thousands of years in many different cultures. Too often, we forget that math has a history, and that it has been developed by and passed on to different cultures in all parts of the world.

This week we conducted a number of experiments that involved probability. Your child has conducted one or two such experiments at home this week. Probability is one of the most misunderstood areas of mathematics, yet one that is constantly in our lives. Advertisers tell us that 3 out of 4 doctors recommend a product without telling us how many doctors were interviewed. Lotteries have become the second leading source of government income, often because people do not understand the probability of winning. Doctors recommend treatments based on percentages, not on certainties, and ask us to make judgements based on these probabilities.

To help your child become more knowledgeable about probability, we conducted experiments involving flipping coins and the use of spinners. We listed all the possible outcomes to determine the likelihood of an event occurring. We discussed the difference between theoretical probability and experimental probability, or comparing what is supposed to occur mathematically with what actually occurs.

Your child has played many games this summer to practice and reinforce math skills. Before the work of this summer fades from memory, have your child make versions of these games that you can play together at home. Playing them for the rest of the summer and through the next year will provide an enjoyable way to continue to practice mathematics.

Mathematics is something we use every day, even if we don't always notice it. Hopefully by looking for examples of math in the world around us, both you and your child are more aware of it. Continue to enjoy math with your child.